$2

Two Houses Down

A Story for Children about Divorce and Friendship

D1496432

By Tiffany Obeng
Illustrations by Ricky Audi

Copyright © 2022 by Tiffany Obeng
All rights reserved. No part of this publication may be reproduced in whole or in part, or stored in a retrieval system, or transmitted in any form or by any means, electronic, mechanical, photocopying, recording or otherwise, without permission of the publisher.

ISBN: 979-8-9855675-4-0
LCCN: 2022900255

Designed by Tiffany Obeng

Other books by Tiffany Obeng:
Andrew Learns about Actors (career book for kids)
Andrew Learns about Teachers (career book for kids)
Andrew Learns about Lawyers (career book for kids)
Andrew Learns about Engineers (career book for kids)
Scout's Honor: A Kid's Book about Lying and Telling the Truth
Winnie Loves Winter: A Delightful Children's Book about Winter
Spencer Knows Spring: A Charming Children's Book about Spring
I Have 10 Toes, Thank You Jesus! (gratitude baby book)

www.SugarCookieBooks.com/Books

Table of Contents

Chapter 1
Saturday

Finally! Saturday had arrived.

Constance climbed out of bed, dressed

in her play clothes, brushed her teeth,

removed her night scarf, and joyfully

skipped down the hall to the kitchen.

"Mommy," Constance said as she sat to eat a crisp golden-brown waffle topped with honey butter, and a small bowl of blueberries.

"You said I could go to Ebony's house to show her my new coloring book on Saturday. It's Saturday. Can I go pretty please?" Constance asked without taking a breath.

Mommy answered, "Of course you can go to your best friend's house.

Finish your breakfast, clean up your space, and you can be on your way."

Constance danced in her chair, wiggling side to side, as she finished her breakfast. *Just three more blueberries, Constance hummed.*

When she had

eaten her last

blueberry,

Constance

exclaimed, "I'm

done!"

Constance rose from her chair and

carefully placed her empty plate and

cup in the sink.

She picked up her coloring book

and box of 64 crayons. Constance and

Ebony always shared crayons.

"Thanks, mommy. See you later!"

Constance said she as left the house.

Chapter 2
Change Is Coming

Mommy watched Constance walk

two houses down to Ebony's house.

Constance rang the doorbell to

Ebony's home. Ebony's mom answered

the door.

Constance greeted, "Hello, Mrs. Johnson. Can Ebony color with me today?" Constance did not see the boxes stacked behind Mrs. Johnson.

Mrs. Johnson turned and called Ebony to the door. Usually, Mrs. Johnson invited Constance right into their home.

Constance saw Ebony walking slowly toward the door. Ebony looked sad.

Constance thought her new

coloring book would surely cheer up

Ebony.

Looking down, Ebony began to

speak in a low voice, "Sorry, today is

not a good day to play. I have to help

my parents pack."

Constance finally saw the boxes

that had been stacked behind Mrs.

Johnson.

Constance asked confused, "Oh,

really? Pack for what?"

Ebony sighed with a shrug, "We

are moving. My parents said they are

getting a divorce."

Divorce? Constance did not

understand what Ebony was saying.

 Constance wanted to ask, but the lump in her throat would not let her words escape.

Constance and Ebony stood frozen and silent as if they were playing the silent game.

Ebony ended the silence and the game, "Okay, well I have to get back to packing. We move in a couple of days.

Talk to you later?"

Constance nodded her head, still

unable to speak.

Ebony slowly closed the door and

Constance slowly walked back to her

home two houses down.

Chapter 3
What Does Divorce Mean?

Constance slowly entered her

home with her head hanging low and

her feet dragging.

Constance mumbled, "Mommy,

I'm back."

Constance went to her bedroom.

She plopped down at her desk and laid

her head into her folded arms.

Mommy walked into Constance's

room. She asked, "Constance, what are

you doing back so soon? What's

wrong?"

Constance's words finally pushed

past the lump in her throat as she

blurted, "Ebony told me they are

moving, and her parents are getting

a divorce."

Constance looked up into

Mommy's eyes searching for answers.

Mommy sat on Constance's bed

nearby. She said, "Oh, really? That

must be tough for Ebony and her

family."

Constance asked nervously, "Mommy, what does divorce mean?"

Mommy answered, "Divorce means that Ebony's parents will no longer live together."

"But why not?" asked Constance.

Mommy answered as best she could. "Well, there are many reasons why people divorce. We will not know their reason, but it seems Ebony's parents have decided that they can provide a happier and more loving home to Ebony if they no longer live together."

Scared, Constance next asked, "Are you getting a divorce?"

Mommy assured Constance, "No,

we are not."

Constance began to sob lightly as she asked, "But why does Ebony have to move, Mommy?"

Mommy explained, "Because her parents will each have a home now, which means Ebony will have two homes. Ebony will have a home that she lives in with one parent and a home that she lives in with the other parent."

Mommy added, "Whichever home Ebony is in, she will always be loved by both parents."

Constance was still confused. "But I still do not get why this is happening to Ebony. Did Ebony do something? Is this punishment for something?"

"No," Mommy answered. "Ebony

did not do anything and none of this is

punishment. "

Chapter 4
Will We Still Be Friends?

Constance cried as she mustered

the courage to ask the next questions:

"Will I ever see Ebony again? Will she

still be my best friend?"

Mommy comforted Constance,

"Sure. We do not know all the details

of Ebony's new living situation yet, but if one of the parent's keep the home two houses down, then you can play with Ebony when she lives at that home."

Mommy explained, "It may not always be as easy as walking two houses down, but you and Ebony can call each other and write to each other when she is not nearby. If they do not move too far away, you may be able to visit her new home."

Mommy moved closer to

Constance. "I want you to know that

it is okay to feel confused or sad or

even angry today or many days to

come. Sometimes, these feelings may

take you by surprise, and that is okay

too."

"And you know, Ebony is really scared, too. This is a lot of change for Ebony, " Mommy told Constance.

"There may be times when Ebony does not want to play. It is not because she does not want to be your friend. Ebony just has a lot going on. So be patient with Ebony as she gets used to her new living situation and life. Be kind to her and try to listen to her if she wants to talk about it. Make sure she knows you love her, wherever she is." Mommy suggested.

Constance agreed, "Okay, mommy. I will."

Then Constance asked her mom, "Do you think Ebony would like a coloring page from my new coloring book for her to take to her new home?"

Constance perked up a bit with the next idea. "Or maybe the coloring book can be both of ours and we take

turns with the coloring book, coloring

a page at a time until it is complete!"

Mommy said, "I think that is a

good idea."

Constance turned toward her desk

and opened her coloring book. She

wiped the tears from her eyes so she could see clearly. Constance flipped to a page with a bear on it because Constance loved cute, cuddly bears.

This will be my best coloring ever, Constance promised Ebony in her heart.

About the Author

Inspired by her own childhood, Tiffany Obeng authored this book from the perspective of her best friend who lived two houses down before Tiffany's parents divorced. Though Tiffany and her best friend reconnected a few times over their childhood years, Tiffany often wondered as an adult, how her parents' divorce might have made her best friend feel. There are plenty of kids' books about divorce, but none like *Two Houses Down*. Tiffany hopes that this story book can be used as a universal tool to talk to all kids about divorce, in order to raise understanding as well as empathy for children of divorced parents.

Follow Tiffany **@SugarCookieBooks** on Instagram and Facebook for behind-the-scenes facts and fun.

Did You Know?

The Bear coloring page illustrated in the book is a real coloring page from a real coloring book: *Animals in the Forest: A Cute Coloring and Activity Book.*

Scan the QR code to request your **FREE** Bear coloring page and other activities from *Animals in the Forest.*

FREE BEAR COLORING PAGE

CPSIA information can be obtained
at www.ICGtesting.com
Printed in the USA
LVHW071539080822
725434LV00001B/12